M000201061

Santa Fe Trail Trivia

SANTA FE
TRAIL

Santa Fe Trail Trivia

Compiled by

Leo E. Oliva

and

Bonita M. Oliva

Third Edition

Western Books
P. O. Box 1
Woodston, KS 67675

1989

Copyright 1989 by

Western Books

ISBN: 0-938463-04-7

Printed in the United States of America
by
Ellsworth Printing Co.
Ellsworth, Kansas

CONTENTS

Front Cover: The Santa Fe Trail map on the cover
was drawn and published by the late Frank A. Cooper
of Lyons, Kansas, and is reproduced here by special
permission of his widow, Velma Cooper Purdy, and
courtesy of the Kansas Heritage Center in Dodge City.
A 16 x 20 print of this map, suitable for framing,
may be obtained from the Kansas Heritage Center,
P. O. Box 1275, Dodge City, KS 67801.

In Memory of
LOUISE BARRY
1910-1974
Research Historian
Trail Scholar

PREFACE

The word "trivia" is used in the title of this booklet only because of the popularity of that format; we do not consider the information to be trivial. The Santa Fe Trail was the oldest and most important overland trail in the history of the American West, and it is a fascinating part of our heritage. The organization of the Santa Fe Trail Association in 1986 and the designation of the route as a part of the National Historic Trails System in 1987 are indicative of a revival of interest in the history and lore of the famous old Trail. An invitation to join the Santa Fe Trail Association is included at the end of this booklet.

The questions and answers included here are designed to create further interest in knowing more about this enchanted road, and a brief list of suggested readings is included to help anyone wanting to know more. The format is designed to be entertaining as well as informative. It can be used by people of all ages and is recommended for travelers as an activity while on the road. The enthusiastic reception of two briefer editions encouraged the compilation of this third edition. Because new information comes to light each year, new questions can be added and some of the answers are different (for example, the identify of the first-known Anglo-American woman to travel the Trail is different in this edition from the answer given in the first two editions).

With thanks, we acknowledge the contributions of the writers of numerous sources utilized in preparing this booklet. It is impossible to name everyone who has contributed information and encouragement, but several persons deserve to be named although they may wish to remain anonymous. We hold none of them responsible for the shortcomings of this endeavor; the mistakes that remain are ours, and they were easy to make and required no help.

We offer thanks to Joseph Snell (Director Emeritus of the Kansas State Historical Society and now Vice-President of the Santa Fe Trail Association) and the staff at the Kansas State Historical Society (especially Colene Bailes and Martin Stein), Ruth Olson and Betsy Crawford Gore at the Santa Fe Trail Center near Larned, Betty Braddock and Noel Ary at the Kansas Heritage Center in Dodge City, Jere Krakow of the National Park Service, Gregory M. Franzwa and his Patrice Press at St. Louis, and a host of Trail aficionados located throughout the region of the historic route (including Paul Bentrup, Robert Button, Mary Jean Cook, Don Cress, Michael Duncan, George Elmore, Richard Forry, Pauline Fowler, Ron and Karla French, Mark Gardner, Pat Heath, Ralph Hathaway, David Hutchison, Katharine Kelley, Stanley Kimball, Brooks Littrell, Marian Meyer, Linda Peters, Joy Poole, Sue Richardson, David Sandoval, Dan and Carol Sharp, Les Vilda, Dave Webb, William Wheatley, Ed White, Evelyn Wilkerson, and Timothy Zwink).

The special permission granted by Velma Cooper Purdy to reproduce the Frank A. Cooper map on the cover is gratefully acknowledged. Our special thanks go to Marc Simmons, first president of the Santa Fe Trail Association and leading Trail scholar, a thoughtful and generous human being, for his willingness to share his vast knowledge with those of us whose understanding is only half-vast. Finally, we avow that much of what is included here was gathered from the late Louise Barry's remarkable compilation, *The Beginning of the West: Annals of the Kansas Gateway to the American West, 1540-1854*, a book which no student of the Trail should be without, and we respectfully dedicate this little booklet to the memory of that tireless researcher and devoted scholar.

If our questions compel you to visit the old Trail or seek further information wherever it may be found, this little booklet will have served a purpose beyond your entertainment and our greed. If you like this booklet, recommend it to your friends. But please don't loan your copy; make them buy their own.

Leo E. and Bonita M. Oliva

Woodston, Kansas
January 1, 1989

SANTA FE TRAIL QUESTIONS

1. On what date did the Santa Fe Trail officially become part of the National Historic Trails System?

2. This classic book on the Santa Fe Trail and trade was first published in 1844?

3. The author of that classic, who made many trips over the Trail, was?

4. The Santa Fe Trail was successfully opened as a commercial route in what year?

5. What major event occurred at each end of the Trail in that momentous year?

6. Who was president of the United States when the Trail was successfully opened?

7. The man credited with opening the Santa Fe Trail to successful commerce and known as "Father of the Trail" was?

8. That "Father of the Trail" may have learned much about the plains country from this fur trader who had traveled across the region along a portion of the Arkansas River and at whose Missouri home the organizational meeting of that first successful trading venture to Santa Fe was held?

9. Who was the governor of New Mexico when that first successful trading venture arrived in Santa Fe?

10. In 1824 the "Father of the Trail" left the Santa Fe trade to become what?

11. He apparently made that decision because?

12. The primary function of the Santa Fe Trail was?

13. During the Mexican War the Trail was used also as?

14. After the Mexican War the Trail was used for yet another purpose, that of?

15. The Army of the West, which traveled the Santa Fe Trail and captured New Mexico and the Southwest during the Mexican War, was led by?

16. The Santa Fe Trail was slowly replaced by railroads, a process completed in what year?

17. Who was president of the United States when the railroad reached Santa Fe?

18. Early in the 1900s the route of the Santa Fe Trail was marked by this organization?

19. Who suggested that this organization mark the Santa Fe Trail?

20. In what town is the marker honoring this person who suggested marking the Trail located?

21. Approximately how many Trail markers were placed along the Trail (in Missouri, Kansas, Colorado, and New Mexico) by that organization?

22. Which state has the most of these markers?

23. Approximately how many are located in the state with the most markers?

24. What Colorado couple searched out the markers in that state, refurbished them, and wrote a book about them titled *Santa Fe Trail Markers in Colorado*?

25. What New Mexico marker was stolen from its original location, later found in Albuquerque, returned to a site near its original location, and rededicated in 1988 by the organization that placed it in the first place?

26. Look at the picture of a Santa Fe Trail marker located on the frontispiece (page facing the title page). These markers were placed on or near what type of buildings along the old Trail?

27. These markers were placed by what organization?

28. In what year were those markers erected?

29. Who was the artist who designed the markers?

30. The first known European to travel a portion of what became the Santa Fe Trail and visit Indians in present Kansas was?

31. That man and his expedition called the land (in present Kansas) they visited by this name?

32. Most evidence indicates that the place visited by that first expedition was located at or near the headwaters of this Kansas stream?

33. The Indians residing there were called?

34. The priest who accompanied that first expedition returned as a missionary to those Indians. He was killed, probably near the route of the later Santa Fe Trail, and is known as the first Christian martyr in Kansas. At least three communities along the Trail have erected monuments to commemorate that priest. His name was?

35. The three communities along the Trail where monuments to that priest have been erected are?

36. The founder of Spanish New Mexico in 1598 was?

37. The Spanish restrictions on trade between New Mexico and outsiders were removed when Mexico achieved independence from Spain, opening the way for the opening of the Santa Fe Trail. Mexican independence was achieved in what year?

38. The original starting point of the Santa Fe Trail in Missouri was the town of?

39. That town was also near the western end of this overland road from St. Charles, Missouri?

40. That town where the two trails connected had been founded on the north side of the Missouri River in what year?

41. The first steamboat up the Missouri River reached that town in what year?

42. What was the name of that steamboat?

43. From that original starting point to Santa Fe was a distance of approximately how many miles?

44. The townsite where the Trail started was so damaged by flooding that a new site was established in what year?

45. The new townsite was called?

46. The town located opposite the original starting point of the Trail on the south side of the Missouri River was?

47. The early traders who left the original starting point of the Santa Fe Trail proceeded along the north bank of the Missouri River to this place before crossing the river?

48. Crossing the river at this point brought the traders to this town on the south bank, which was also a point of departure for some traders?

49. The early Santa Fe traders usually followed this older Missouri Trail to Fort Osage?

50. In the 1830s that particular Trail became known as?

51. Another Missouri town, founded on the south bank of the Missouri River in 1822, with a connection to that Trail to Fort Osage, was a landing point for goods shipped upstream to be loaded on wagons bound for Santa Fe. This town was?

52. An important trading firm which outfitted many Santa Fe traders was located at this town and owned and operated by these three brothers?

53. These brothers had branch stores in three other Missouri towns. The three towns were?

54. During the Mexican War, one of the brothers (James) established a store in this Mexican city, where he was killed during a robbery in 1847?

55. Prior to the introduction of steamboats on the Missouri River, how were commodities transported upstream to be loaded on wagons?

56. Many Santa Fe travelers carried the anti-fever pills of this Arrow Rock, Missouri physician?

57. A portrait of that physician, painted by this famous Arrow Rock artist, still hangs in the Old Tavern in Arrow Rock?

58. The son-in-law of that physician, an important Santa Fe trader and later governor of Missouri, was?

59. The U. S. government survey of the Santa Fe Trail began in what year?

60. The survey began at what point in Missouri?

61. That place had been founded in what year?

62. It had been founded by?

63. Its original purpose had been?

64. The man in charge of that operation was?

65. That place had also served as a?

66. The Santa Fe Trail survey commission was led by?

67. The engineer who conducted the survey was?

68. The survey party was apparently assisted in its efforts by this former Santa Fe trader?

69. What happened to the field notes and maps of the survey?

70. The history of the Trail survey was written by?

71. The title of that history is?

72. A few miles upstream from the point of origin of the survey was a place originally known as Owens Landing but later known as?

73. A few miles west of Owens Landing was another landing where goods from boats could be deposited to be loaded on wagons. It was?

74. Founded on the Missouri River a little farther west in 1827, this town became an important outfitting point for the Santa Fe traders, superseding all points to the east?

75. That town, with a courthouse square, was the seat of what Missouri county?

76. This man had a blacksmith shop in that town at the corner of what were to be Liberty and Kansas streets?

77. In the 1840s that bustling Missouri community was also the outfitting point for wagons bound for these two other western destinations?

78. This town a little farther west, later engulfed by Kansas City, became a major point of departure for Santa Fe traders during the 1840s and superseded other outfitting points in the 1850s?

79. South of that town with its important river landing, another branch of the Trail crossed the Big Blue River, beyond which a camp located nearly on the western boundary of Missouri developed, later to be known as?

80. Raytown, Missouri, grew around the site of a blacksmith shop located on the Santa Fe Trail by this man in the 1840s?

81. Located near the western edge of modern Raytown was this spring, where early Trail travelers stopped for water and rest?

82. Following construction of a bridge over the Big Blue River, about 15 miles southwest of Independence, Missouri, in 1859, this Trail crossing became known as?

83. Just west of that Big Blue River Crossing, excellent Trail remains can still be seen in this Kansas City park?

84. Founded on the Kansas side of the Missouri River in 1827, this fort was closely associated with the Santa Fe Trail as long as the Trail was used?

85. The early road from that fort to the main Santa Fe Trail, considered to be one of the important branches of the Trail, crossed the Kansas River on this ferry (the first ferry across the Kansas River)?

86. This log tavern was located on the Trail approximately six miles west of Arrow Rock, Missouri, in 1837?

87. Originally called Round Grove before most of the timber was cut, this was a much-used campsite in present eastern Kansas (sometimes the point of rendezvous)?

88. 110-Mile Creek was so named because it was 110 miles from?

89. Before that distance had been calculated, 110-Mile Creek had been known as?

90. This man built a toll bridge and stage station at 110-Mile Creek in 1854?

91. This town, originally called Council City when founded in 1857, claims (incorrectly) to be the only town in Kansas with a main street that was once part of the Santa Fe Trail?

92. That town is located on what was originally called Bridge Creek but was later known by the name of the man who constructed a toll bridge there in 1847. What was his name and what is the name of the creek?

93. In 1859 that toll bridge was owned and operated by?

94. The next creek westward was probably named to honor a military expedition of mounted soldiers (exact date unknown); the creek is called?

95. A small tributary of that creek received its name when 38 soldiers from Fort Leavenworth died there from cholera in 1851. This tributary is still known as?

96. An important point of rendezvous on the Santa Fe Trail at the crossing of the Neosho River, this campground and later town took its name following a treaty council there with the Osages in 1825?

97. A treaty council with the Kansa Indians was held that same year near the Santa Fe Trail on this creek?

98. This great-grandson of Daniel Boone established a trading post at the Neosho River Crossing in 1847?

99. Some of the finest remains of Santa Fe Trail ruts found anywhere along the Trail are visible on the land of this farmer northwest of Chase, Kansas?

100. About a mile west of those outstanding ruts were these famous sandhills, no longer there?

101. The Santa Fe Trail followed the valley of this river through much of western Kansas?

102. Many travelers crossed that river in western Kansas and headed south on the "Desert Route" to this river?

103. Those who followed the "Mountain Route" continued westward to this famous trading fort in present eastern Colorado?

104. Those who followed the "Desert Route" had many opportunities to cross the river. Lower Crossing, east of present Dodge City, was located where this creek entered from the south?

105. The Middle Crossings were located west of Dodge City near (perhaps between) these two present Kansas towns?

106. The Upper Crossing was located near this famous island southwest of present Lakin, Kansas?

107. The Upper Crossing and that island were located near this landmark (a lookout point used by Indians and traders) which may still be seen?

108. Regardless of the crossing, the route to the Cimarron River was often without water, and this section of the Trail was known as the Cimarron Desert or?

109. The route across the Cimarron Desert was not clearly marked until this year of heavy rains, before which time caravans sometimes became lost and

missed the Lower Spring of the Cimarron River?

110. The Hispanic towns of New Mexico were usually built around this central feature?

111. This campsite (and, later, stage station) about ten miles southeast of Santa Fe was the last stop on the road to Santa Fe, a point where Trail travelers cleaned up before entering the city of their destination?

112. These French brothers traveled across the plains to Santa Fe in 1739?

113. These three French deserters from the French Post on the Arkansas River traveled overland to Santa Fe in 1748?

114. This native of Spain who was at the French Post on the Arkansas River traveled overland to Santa Fe in 1749-1750?

115. Jean Chapuis and Luis Feuilli, two Frenchmen, traveled overland to Pecos Mission in New Mexico in 1752 from this French trading fort on the west side of the Missouri River near present Fort Leavenworth, Kansas?

116. This French native who became a citizen of Spain traveled from St. Louis to Santa Fe in 1793, following a portion of what later was known as the Santa Fe Trail?

117. He had gone from Santa Fe to St. Louis the previous year, accompanied by these two men?

118. The first known traders to take goods from the United States to Santa Fe, in 1804, were?

119. Sent to explore a portion of the Louisiana Purchase in 1806, this famous officer and some of his troops were captured and taken to Santa Fe?

120. Who sent that officer on his exploring expedition?

121. The Spanish governor of New Mexico, warned of this exploring expedition, sent a large body of troops onto the plains to try to counter the U. S. expedition. The Spanish troops were led by?

122. The American exploring expedition was accompanied by this physician, who may have been sent to help spy out Spanish authority in New Mexico?

123. This trader, who took goods to Santa Fe in 1807,

was considered "the first American trader to earn profits on a trip to Santa Fe"?

124. These four men led a trading party to Santa Fe in 1812, and they were taken captive and imprisoned in Chihuahua until 1821?

125. This 19-year-old adventurer and his Black companion, Alfred, traveled to New Mexico in 1820, searching for a wagon route to Santa Fe, only to be captured and imprisoned for a time?

126. This young man and Alfred had traveled to New Mexico in company with a party of?

127. He was held prisoner in the Palace of the Governors; ironically, he returned to Santa Fe via the Santa Fe Trail in 1853 to assume this office?

128. What unusual event occurred at the time he took that office?

129. This young Virginian was imprisoned in Santa Fe in 1773, following capture of the ship he was on near the mouth of the Rio Grande?

130. He was accompanied on the trip and in jail by his part-Indian servant named?

131. These two prisoners made their escape from the Santa Fe jail with the help of the jailer's daughter, who fell in love with the servant. She was?

132. The prisoners and the jailer's daughter crossed the plains, perhaps following a portion of the future Santa Fe Trail, and reached this settlement on the Mississippi River in 1774?

133. Santa Fe, New Mexico, is the oldest capital city in the United States. In what year was it founded?

134. What is the full name of that New Mexican capital?

135. What is the English translation of that name?

136. On what river is the city of Santa Fe located?

137. The oldest non-Indian public structure still in use in the United States is the?

138. That historic building is located where?

139. The oldest non-Indian church in the United States is located in Santa Fe. It is?

140. What type of building construction was introduced into the American Southwest by the Spanish?

141. What ancient New Mexico Indian pueblo, situated on the Santa Fe Trail, was abandoned by its remaining residents in 1837?

142. The special structure used by the Pueblo Indians for religious purposes was the?

143. The Pueblo Indians drove the Spaniards out of New Mexico in the famed Pueblo Revolt of what year?

144. The leader of the Pueblo Revolt was?

145. Who was the Spanish general who accomplished the reconquest of Santa Fe in 1692?

146. Who is the benefactress responsible for construction of the beautiful visitors' center and museum at Pecos Pueblo National Historic Site?

147. These two men led a trading party from Fort Smith, Arkansas, to Santa Fe in 1821, where they arrived only two weeks after the first successful trading party led by "the father of the Santa Fe Trail," seeking not only trade but the party that had gone to Santa Fe in 1812 and was believed to be still imprisoned there?

148. The first wagons were taken over the Santa Fe Trail in what year?

149. From what point in Missouri did those wagons began that trip?

150. Who organized that wagon trip?

151. According to a Missouri newspaper, he paid $150 for a wagon in Missouri and sold it in Santa Fe for how much?

152. During the early years of the Santa Fe trade, these famous wagons, manufactured in Pennsylvania, were used on the Trail?

153. These famous wagons, and several variations manufactured in Missouri, had arched bows over the box which was covered with a type of canvas known as?

154. A larger freight wagon designed for use on the Trail, manufactured at St Louis and, possibly, other Missouri towns, was the?

155. The wagons could haul approximately how many pounds of payload?

156. Most freight wagons were painted with two colors. The common color used on the wagon boxes was?

157. The common color used on the running gear and wheels was?

158. The wagon wheels were lubricated by a mixture of these two items, carried in a special bucket suspended under the wagon bed?

159. The forward team of the draft animals pulling a wagon were known as the?

160. The rear team hitched direct to the wagon were known as the?

161. The other teams located between the front and rear teams were known as?

162. The command to turn the draft animals to the left was?

163. The command to turn the draft animals to the right was?

164. The command to stop the draft animals was?

165. These two men led a party of traders who went to Taos rather than Santa Fe during the winter of 1821-1822?

166. One of the members of that Taos-bound party, Lewis Dawson, may have been the first casualty of the Santa Fe trade when he was killed near the Purgatoire River in present Colorado by?

167. James Baird and Samuel Chambers led a trading expedition on the Santa Fe Trail late in 1822 and were caught in a blizzard west of present Dodge City where they were forced to spend the winter. They dug large pits to store their trade goods, and the place became this well-known landmark?

168. A trading party led by Stephen Cooper in 1823 followed the Cimarron Route, where they became so thirsty from lack of water that they reportedly drank what?

169. The traders who traveled the road to Santa Fe in 1824 took some of their trade items to markets in this Mexican community?

170. This trader from Missouri supplied Senator Thomas H. Benton with detailed information about the Santa Fe Trail and trade in 1824, which was

published by Congress. This same trader was later appointed U. S. Consul at Santa Fe?

171. Another Missouri trader in the 1824 caravan, who later served as governor of Missouri, provided the first detailed account of the difficult crossing of the Cimarron Desert; he was?

172. It was later reported that the 1824 caravan carried a cannon for protection but abandoned it near this site when it became a burden?

173. Early traders had to pay customs duties on all goods taken into Mexico. These duties were for a time collected at this village?

174. That village had the distinction of being the southernmost point of the?

175. That village was located on what river?

176. Customs duties in 1825 amounted to what percent of the value of the goods?

177. In later years customs duties were assessed at so much per wagon, regardless of the cargo, and varied widely from year to year but ranging from about $_____ to $_____ for each wagon?

178. The practice of charging so much per wagon caused traders to do what?

179. In order to provide better protection while traveling the Trail, the wagons of several proprietors began organizing caravans. The first caravan traveled the Trail in what year?

180. That first caravan was organized at this point, located about ten miles southwest of Fort Osage?

181. The head officer, elected to direct the travel and safety of a caravan, was called the?

182. Just as the Neosho River was a point of rendezvous and organizing point for many caravans going west, this stream in New Mexico served a similar place for caravans going east from Santa Fe?

183. The availability of these three items was essential for a good campsite on the Trail?

184. In 1825 at least nine Plains Indian tribes agreed not to molest American citizens who traveled the Santa Fe Trail; name them.

185. The government survey of the Santa Fe Trail in

1825 proceeded to this point on the Arkansas River and did not continue until permission was obtained from the government of Mexico?

186. The survey in Mexican territory worked from New Mexico to the Arkansas River, but instead of running from Santa Fe the surveyors measured from this town in New Mexico?

187. This man, who was injured in a gun accident, had his arm amputated while at the Walnut Creek camp of an 1826 Santa Fe Trail caravan, the operation being performed with a knife and saw and cauterized with a heated wagon bolt, all of which he survived?

188. Who performed that surgery?

189. Christopher "Kit" Carson escaped his Missouri apprenticeship by traveling the Santa Fe Trail to New Mexico, where he became a "mountain man" and married a native named?

190. For a time the Carsons lived in this New Mexico town?

191. Today the Carson home there is a museum, as is the home of this famous Santa Fe trader who died there in 1847?

192. In 1841 Bent had hired Kit Carson to help hunt buffalo and other animals for meat for Bent's Fort, for which Carson earned how much money per day?

193. A portion of the government survey of 1825 was resurveyed in 1827, and this famous spring located approximately 15 miles west of Council Grove, previously known as "Jones' Spring" was given this descriptive name by which it is still known?

194. East of Council Grove, this spring, originally called Big John Spring, was renamed to honor a western explorer?

195. Lost Spring stage station was won by this cowboy in a poker game in 1866?

196. The stone corral, probably associated with a trading station, was located near the Trail crossing of what river?

197. This army paymaster traveled the road to Santa Fe and on to Chihuahua in 1828 and wrote his observations which aided future travelers and the military?

198. According to his own diary, that army paymaster did what on July 1, 1828, while engaged in a buffalo chase?

199. Major items taken to New Mexico over the Santa Fe Trail were?

200. This famous trade item, valued by Indians and Hispanics, was marked in points to indicate its value in beaver pelts?

201. Major items taken from New Mexico to Missouri over the Trail were?

202. Three or four beaver pelts were needed to manufacture this prized fashion item?

203. Although the cost of freighting items over the Santa Fe Trail varied from year to year and depended on the type of commodity, the average cost during the first three decades of the trade was about?

204. The first printing press in New Mexico was hauled over the Santa Fe Trail in what year?

205. That press was put to use in Taos by this priest?

206. The first newspaper in New Mexico, printed on that press, was?

207. The first newspaper in Santa Fe that lasted over a period of years was founded in 1851 by this former Santa Fe trader?

208. His Santa Fe newspaper was the?

209. The founder of that newspaper was murdered during the robbery of his office in Santa Fe in what year?

210. The first steam engine in New Mexico was freighted over the Santa Fe Trail in what year?

211. What animals were used to pull wagons on the Santa Fe Trail?

212. Of these draft animals, which were used most during the history of the Trail?

213. Which draft animals were used least?

214. What were the orders issued to get the wagons hitched and ready to travel?

215. What was the shout to start the wagons on the road?

216. What was the average salary paid to the teamsters who drove the wagons to Santa Fe?

217. What items comprised the diet of the teamsters?

218. What two insects plagued those traveling the Trail?

219. In how many columns did Santa Fe Trail wagon trains usually travel, depending on the terrain?

220. On average, how many miles per day did a caravan travel?

221. These two men, killed on the Trail by Indians in 1828, were buried along the Trail; the name of one was given to a crossing in New Mexico where the attack occurred?

222. That crossing in New Mexico is located on the North Canadian River, earlier known as?

223. Today that creek is known locally as?

224. This captain of a caravan returning from Santa Fe was killed by Indians near Upper Cimarron Spring in 1828?

225. The first military escort for traders on the Trail, in 1829, was led by?

226. The military escort of 1829 introduced these draft animals to the Trail?

227. The men who drove those animals were called?

228. These two famous brothers from Missouri, who were to play an important role in the history of the Trail and the Southwest, were members of the 1829 caravan (one was captain)?

229. Soon after the 1829 caravan crossed the Arkansas River into Mexican territory, leaving the military escort behind, Indians attacked the traders and killed this Missouri trader?

230. The caravan returning from Santa Fe in 1829 was accompanied by Mexican troops, led by this Mexican officer?

231. This Santa Fe trader single-handedly drove 40 mules from New Mexico to Missouri in 1830?

232. This famous mountain man and fur trader entered the Santa Fe trade in 1831 and was killed by Indians somewhere on the Cimarron River, perhaps near Wagon Bed Spring or Fargo Spring, in that year?

233. Wagon Bed Spring, located on the Cimarron River, had originally been known as?

234. Wagon Bed Spring was usually the point where routes from these two crossings of the Arkansas River rejoined?

235. What holiday was celebrated near McNees Crossing in New Mexico in 1831, an event commemorated by a marker at the site?

236. The military escort for the Santa Fe traders in 1833 included troops of this new regiment, perhaps created because of the inadequacy of infantry soldiers in dealing with mounted Plains Indians?

237. The commanding officer of the escort in 1833 was?

238. The military escort for the Santa Fe traders in 1834 included troops of this new regiment, successor to the regiment which provided escort troops in 1833?

239. The commanding officer of the escort in 1834 was?

240. Who led the 1835 Dragoon expedition from Fort Leavenworth to the Rocky Mountains that returned via the Santa Fe Trail?

241. The only casualty on that 1835 Dragoon expedition died along the Trail, and his lonely grave with stone marker may still be seen west of Burlingame. He was Pvt.?

242. Another gravesite, located in present McPherson County, Kansas, near the old Trail was for this young man who was killed by Cheyenne Indians in 1864?

243. This actor and newspaper correspondent traveled the Trail in 1839 and kept a journal which was later published along with other "sketches" of the region?

244. This German traveler over the Santa Fe Trail in 1839 published a book in his native language about his adventures, which was later translated into English?

245. In 1841 Manuel Alvarez and his small wagon train suffered through a blizzard at the crossing of this river, losing two men and all the mules?

246. Ten years later, at the same crossing, a military expedition led by this officer lost one man and about 300 mules to another blizzard?

247. In October and November of 1852 this physician

traveled the Santa Fe Trail to New Mexico to assume his post as agent to the Mescalero Apaches?

248. His party survived a severe snow storm which struck them while using this new route from the Arkansas to the Cimarron rivers?

249. That physician reported that his party saved their mules by?

250. In August of 1842 a Missouri River steamboat carrying the merchandise of several Santa Fe traders sank some 50 miles below Independence, resulting in the loss of $80,000 in goods. The steamboat was the?

251. This Mexican trader, also the governor of New Mexico, lost about $20,000 worth of goods when that boat sank?

252. The Republic of Texas attempted the conquest of New Mexico with the ill-fated Texan-Santa Fe Expedition in what year?

253. Who led the Texan force?

254. This reporter for the New Orleans *Picayune* accompanied the expedition and provided detailed reports?

255. That reporter published a book about the experiences in 1844, *Narrative of the Texan-Santa Fe Expedition*, which was later referred to by some historians as the _____ of the Mexican War?

256. Who was the governor of New Mexico at the time who defeated the Texans?

257. This Mexican trader was killed by Texas partisans near the Trail on a tributary of Cow Creek in present Rice County, Kansas (which tributary was named after the trader) in 1843?

258. The leader of those Texas partisans who operated from Missouri and who was hanged for the murder of the Mexican trader was?

259. Because of the threat of Texan raiders on Mexican traders in 1843, a military escort was sent out with the spring caravan from Missouri. The commander of the escort was?

260. Because of an inscription in the rock near this spring, stating "U.S. Post 1843," that military es-

cort may have camped at this site?

261. This spring 1843 military escort captured a band of Texan raiders near this present Kansas town?

262. The leader of the Texan raiders captured there was?

263. That party of Texan raiders had been joined by some men from another Texan raiding expedition that attacked the small settlement on the Mora River in New Mexico that same year and had been driven off by a New Mexican force. The leader of that raid was?

264. The fall 1843 caravan to Santa Fe, an all Mexican train, was accompanied by a U. S. military escort led by?

265. This year of excessive rainfall in Kansas, which produced big floods, caused delays of several weeks at stream crossings for traders returning from Santa Fe and delayed the caravans going to Santa Fe until August?

266. An expedition of First Dragoons marched to the Rocky Mountains over the Oregon Trail and returned over the Santa Fe Trail in 1845. They departed from and returned to what fort?

267. The commander of that 1845 expedition was?

268. That 1845 military expedition traveled _____ miles?

269. That 1845 military expedition was on the road _____ days?

270. How many soldiers on that 1845 expedition died during the trip?

271. One important issue of contention between the United States traders and Mexican authorities, regarding the trade prior to the Mexican War, was?

272. The first year that the Mountain Branch via Raton Pass was used extensively by wagons was?

273. In that year these two army lieutenants were sent from Bent's Fort to make a survey of Raton Pass, the Canadian River, and other streams, on the way to Fort Gibson in present Oklahoma?

274. They were guided by this famous mountain man and fur trader?

275. In that same year this famous army explorer traveled westward from Bent's Fort to California?

276. One of the guides on this expedition was this famous mountain man and fur trader?

277. Prior to that time, travelers using the Mountain Route probably crossed the mountains by this pass, which led them past modern Folsom, New Mexico?

278. The route of the Trail through that pass was commonly known as?

279. That route had been marked by an army officer in what year?

280. The officer who located the route was?

281. That branch of the Trail left the Arkansas River a few miles west of this present-day Colorado town?

282. That particular branch of the Trail may have seen its heaviest use during the years 1873-1875 when this Colorado town was the freight terminus of the Atchison, Topeka and Santa Fe Railroad?

283. That branch rejoined the main Santa Fe Trail in New Mexico near the?

284. The Army of the West used Raton Pass as the route of invasion and made many improvements on it in what year?

285. The Raton Pass route was used during the remainder of the Mexican War but was little used by Santa Fe Trail traffic again until?

286. The major reason the Mountain Route was promoted then was because the Cimarron Cutoff was unsafe due to hostile threats from these two Indian tribes?

287. During the Civil War troops at Forts Larned and Union provided escorts to wagon trains traveling between those two posts via Raton Pass, with help from this military post located between Larned and Union?

288. The road over Raton Pass was much improved when this man opened a toll road there?

289. The proprietor of that toll road was commonly known as?

290. His toll road opened in what year?

291. The toll for use of the Raton Pass road was how much per wagon?

292. All Trail travelers and loose livestock were charged to use the toll road, but the proprietor permitted one group of people to pass freely. Those not having to pay were?

293. The Mountain Route from Bent's Fort to Raton Pass followed a portion of the valley of this tributary of the Arkansas River?

294. A landmark on the Trail on Timpas Creek near present Thatcher, Colorado, was?

295. That landmark on Timpas Creek was destroyed by what?

296. A landmark on the Trail near present Tyrone, Colorado, was?

297. This town grew along side the Trail near the north entrance to Raton Pass?

298. This landmark overlooks the northern entrance to Raton Pass?

299. The marked grave of this person, murdered on the Trail, is located at Raton Pass?

300. This town grew along side the Trail near the south entrance to Raton Pass?

301. The town near the south entrance to Raton Pass developed around these springs on the Trail?

302. Southwest of Raton Pass, near the Mountain Branch crossing of the Canadian River, there was a three-story adobe trading post and stage station known as?

303. In 1865 this army general, in command of the troops in New Mexico, established an escort system over the Trail, utilizing troops from Forts Larned and Union, which alternated biweekly escorts between the Mountain and Cimarron branches?

304. At the same time this army general in Kansas added a connecting escort system between Fort Larned and Council Grove?

305. In all, those escort systems on the Trail in 1865 utilized troops from these six Trail forts?

306. When that escort system appeared to be placing

too much demand on the number of soldiers available, yet another military post was established in the present Oklahoma panhandle; this new post was?

307. This physician, who engaged in the Santa Fe trade and traveled the Trail, married the daughter of a New Mexico governor?

308. The maiden name of this physician's wife was?

309. She was one of the early women travelers on the Santa Fe Trail, traveling with her husband in what year?

310. The Santa Fe Trail was considered to end in the plaza of Santa Fe, located in the southwestern state whose motto is?

311. This Santa Fe trader, famous for his record-setting rides on horseback over the route, had a cutoff from the Arkansas River to the Cimarron River and a fort named after him?

312. The record horseback ride, from Santa Fe to Independence, was made by that trader in how much time?

313. Although most Americans thought that the Santa Fe Trail ended at Santa Fe, it actually connected with another Trail which ran far into Mexico. That Trail was known as?

314. The trade with Santa Fe was originally opened by traders from Missouri, but Mexican traders were active in that international trade after what year?

315. Who was probably the first Mexican to outfit wagons in Missouri and transport trade items over the Trail to Santa Fe?

316. In 1839 this Spaniard, who had earlier immigrated to Mexico and then to the United States where he became a Santa Fe trader, was appointed to the office of U. S. consul in Santa Fe (in which office he served even though the Mexican government never gave him official recognition)?

317. As trade increased many caravan traders began to purchase commodities directly from eastern wholesale firms; the available records for the early 1840s indicate that 2/3 of the wholesale firms dealt with were located in this eastern city?

318. Most of the other wholesale firms dealt with were

located in this eastern city?

319. Many of the Mexican merchants engaged in the Santa Fe trade dealt with this Spanish firm located in New York City?

320. Early travelers on the Trail stopped at the ranch of Luis Maria Cabeza de Vaca in New Mexico soon after crossing into the drainage of the Rio Grande. This was the location of what springs and river?

321. That location later became this Trail town?

322. In what year was that town founded?

323. The range of mountains in New Mexico through which the Trail had to pass to reach Santa Fe is the?

324. The name means what?

325. The pass the Trail followed through the mountains to Santa Fe is?

326. This young Bostonian, who visited the West in 1846 and wrote a classic book titled *The Oregon Trail*, traveled the Santa Fe Trail from Bent's Fort to the Missouri River that same year?

327. On May 13, 1846, the United States declared war against what nation?

328. Who was president of the United States during that war?

329. Who was the secretary of war for the United States during that war?

330. Brig. Gen. Stephen Watts Kearny led a military force over the Santa Fe Trail during the Mexican War and captured Santa Fe and other points in the Southwest. His military force was known as?

331. The commander of the First Regiment of Missouri Volunteers raised to march with Kearny's force over the Santa Fe Trail was?

332. A large statue honoring that commander of Missouri troops is located in this Missouri town?

333. Kearny's Army followed which branch of the Trail to New Mexico?

334. Kearny's Army assembled at this trading post prior to the invasion of Mexican territory?

335. This lieutenant of the Corps of Topographical Engineers was attached to Kearny's Army to gather information on the Southwest, which resulted in a map and report on the region?

336. The peaceful occupation of Santa Fe was accomplished on what date?

337. Who was the Mexican governor of New Mexico who retreated without a battle?

338. This wealthy Santa Fe woman, reportedly a prostitute and one of the wealthiest people in Santa Fe, not only provided capital for merchandise carried over the Santa Fe Trail, but she also provided necessary funds for supplies for American troops who invaded Chihuahua from New Mexico during the Mexican War?

339. What was her nickname, by which she was commonly known?

340. By this treaty, signed in 1848, Mexico ceded much of the American Southwest to the United States?

341. Following the Mexican War, commerce over the Santa Fe Trail increased rapidly as Anglo-Americans moved to the Southwest. The value of commodities carried over the Trail was estimated at $_____ in 1855?

342. A number of Jewish immigrants from Germany entered the Santa Fe trade and became merchants in New Mexico. A notable example of such a firm in the 1860s was operated in Santa Fe by these brothers?

343. Total sales of their firm in Santa Fe during the life of the company have been estimated at what value?

344. One of those brothers was one of the founders of this significant organization, the first such organization west of the Mississippi River?

345. In what year was that organization founded at Santa Fe?

346. By 1859 the value of commodities carried over the Trail was estimated at $_____?

347. By 1862 the value of commodities carried over the Trail was estimated at $_____?

348. The soldiers who marched over the Santa Fe Trail

during the Mexican War, as well as other travelers along that route, frequently suffered from this disease?

349. The cause of this disease was a lack of this item in their diet?

350. What ingredient in Mexican cooking cured that disease?

351. Military freighting on the Trail was big business after the war with?

352. After that war, the government turned to the contract system for military freighting; in 1848 a contract was let to this freighter from Independence, Missouri?

353. That contract provided for what rate per hundred pounds from Fort Leavenworth to New Mexico?

354. In 1849 the contract on the Trail went to these Missouri partners?

355. These two Missouri traders entered the military contract freighting business on the Trail in 1850?

356. In 1853 this famous Missouri freighter entered the military contract business on the Trail, on which he had been freighting since 1848, and was later known as the greatest freighter on the Trail?

357. By the late 1850s this Missouri-based freighting firm dominated military contract freighting on the Trail?

358. The first headquarters of that famous freighting firm were located in this Missouri town?

359. What is unique about the courthouse in that Missouri town?

360. Teamsters who worked for that freighting company signed an oath not to drink or curse, and they were paid at what rate?

361. The first women to travel on the Santa Fe Trail were undoubtedly Indian and Hispanic-American, but the first Anglo-American woman known to have traveled the Santa Fe Trail was?

362. In what year did she first travel from Missouri to Santa Fe on the Trail?

363. She and her husband were accompanied by their one-year-old daughter, presumed to be the first

Anglo-American child to travel the Trail. The daughter's name was?

364. While the "first woman on the Trail" and her family lived in Santa Fe, what did they do?

365. While residing in Santa Fe, the "first family on the Trail" had two more children, believed to be the first Anglo-American children born in New Mexico. There names were?

366. In what year did this "first family on the Trail" travel from Santa Fe to Missouri on the Trail?

367. On that trip to Missouri, the "first family on the Trail" was reportedly accompanied by three other Anglo-American women who had been held captive by Indians but had reached freedom at Santa Fe. Those three women were?

368. This young woman, wife of a Santa Fe trader, traveled the road to Santa Fe in 1846, was long believed to have been the first Anglo-American woman to travel the Trail, and her diary was later published under the title *Down the Santa Fe Trail*?

369. Her grandfather had been one of the pioneers of Kentucky, and he was the first governor of that state. He was a famous man in his time, and he died the same year (1826) as Thomas Jefferson and John Adams, and his death was memorialized nationally along with those two famous presidents. He was?

370. This woman traveled the Santa Fe Trail several times as a child and wrote of her experiences in a superb book, *Land of Enchantment*?

371. Her mother operated a boarding house near Santa Fe Plaza where this building now stands?

372. What was the girl called by her friend Christopher (Kit) Carson when he showed her around Santa Fe?

373. This girl later grew up and married an army officer in the chapel at?

374. Later, this woman and her husband, retired from the military, operated a trading post at this New Mexico village?

375. After her many experiences along the Santa Fe Trail and a long, productive life, the author of *Land of Enchantment* died as the result of being struck

by an automobile on the streets of this Trail town in 1936?

376. Three Pioneer Mother statues, erected by the DAR, are located along the Santa Fe Trail in these towns?

377. A fourth Pioneer Mother statue was intended for Santa Fe, New Mexico, but because of opposition to it there the statue was instead placed where?

378. The first woman to climb Pike's Peak, a bloomer-wearing feminist from Kansas who traveled a portion of the Trail to Colorado in 1858, was?

379. She also lived in New Mexico, where her husband served as this public official?

380. His name was?

381. This artist traveled with the 1846 caravan to Santa Fe?

382. This talented soldier of the quartermaster department, who designed and built much of Fort Scott, served as Gen. Kearny's quartermaster during the Mexican War, making use of the Santa Fe Trail as a route of supply?

383. This Santa Fe trader and former U. S. Consul to Chihuahua was sent on a special, secret mission to Santa Fe ahead of the troops to seek a peaceful conquest of the region during the Mexican War?

384. That "secret agent" for the president of the United States helped open the way for the bloodless conquest of Santa Fe, in part, because he was married to a cousin of New Mexico's governor. His wife's maiden name was?

385. That trader and "secret agent" was accompanied to Santa Fe for negotiations by this military officer from Kearny's command?

386. The governor of New Mexico was apparently persuaded to offer no effective resistance to the invading army, but the lieutenant-governor was not so easily persuaded; the lieutenant-governor was?

387. When promises made to that lieutenant-governor were not kept, he helped foment an uprising against United States officials in New Mexico in 1847, known as the?

388. This American physician who had spent much time in Mexico, becoming a citizen of that nation, assist-

ed Kearny and other officials in persuading the New Mexican military to retreat rather than resist the invading army?

389. That physician was a leading merchant in Mexico before the Mexican War and later headed the largest mercantile business in New Mexico. During the Civil War he held this office in New Mexico?

390. That physician had married the widow of this prominent Mexican trader, following that trader's death in 1845?

391. The maiden name of the widow who married the physician was?

392. These two Missouri traders, partners who had apparently made good profits in the trade with Mexico, were killed during the Mexican War in Chihuahua (one in battle and the other at the hands of robbers)?

393. These two Missouri traders, although captured and imprisoned by Mexican officials and fined heavily for their trading activities during wartime, managed to dispose of their trade goods in northern Mexico at wartime profits?

394. A blacksmith and repair shop was established at this famous point on the Santa Fe Trail in 1846 by the army?

395. The Second Regiment of Missouri Volunteers during the Mexican War, outfitted at Fort Leavenworth and marched over the Trail to Santa Fe, was commanded by this Missouri citizen who later was a Confederate general during the Civil War?

396. This infantry battalion, recruited from one particular religious group which was at that time migrating westward from Illinois, marched over the Trail to New Mexico and on to California during the Mexican War?

397. That battalion followed this branch of the Santa Fe Trail?

398. The officer who led that battalion from Santa Fe to California, opening a wagon road which was named to honor him, was?

399. The first U. S. governor of the newly acquired province of New Mexico was this famous trader, who was killed in Taos during the uprising in 1847?

400. This famous Mountain Man served as a guide to Gen. Kearny's army to Santa Fe in 1846, and he was appointed the first U.S. Indian agent to the Indians living along the western portion of the Trail later that same year?

401. A small, stockaded government depot was erected near the Caches by quartermaster teamsters in 1847, and named to honor one of the teamsters. This "first fort" on the Santa Fe Trail was?

402. Some Santa Fe traders opened a trading post at Council Grove in 1847, placing this man in charge (his name is still honored in Council Grove)?

403. In 1856 this merchant moved to Council Grove, where he operated the famous "Stone Store" for several years?

404. Another famous store established in Council Grove, in 1857, the stone building of which still stands as a historic landmark in this community of Trail landmarks, carried this name because it was considered the last point to purchase supplies on the road to Santa Fe?

405. The "Indian Battalion" of Missouri Volunteers was raised to help protect the Santa Fe Trail in 1847. The commander of this unit was?

406. The "Indian Battalion" spent part of its year of service at this post on the Trail?

407. The discovery of this in California in 1848 had a long-term effect on the Santa Fe Trail?

408. The woman, who was disguised as a man and mustered into the "Indian Battalion" in 1847 and was discovered when she became pregnant, was?

409. Most of the DAR markers erected along the Santa Fe Trail in the early 1900s cost how much apiece?

410. In 1855 this noted Santa Fe Trail figure and a long-time associate of the Bent brothers moved to the town of Mora, New Mexico, and opened a grist mill and store?

411. This famous Black Mountain Man was active on the Santa Fe Trail in the late 1840s?

412. This dreaded disease swept down the Santa Fe Trail in 1849 and again in 1867, taking a heavy toll

each time?

413. This famous trading post on the Santa Fe Trail was destroyed by its owner in 1849?

414. In 1849 this merchant from Independence was killed by Apaches near Point of Rocks, New Mexico, and his wife and daughter were captured and later murdered?

415. This military fort, located west of present Dodge City, was founded in 1850 and used until 1854?

416. In 1852 the Catholic Vicar Apostolic of New Mexico traveled to New Mexico via the Santa Fe Trail, accompanied by four Sisters of Loretto. This was the famous Bishop _____, later the subject of Willa Cather's *Death Comes for the Archbishop?*

417. That same bishop was traveling the Trail in 1867 with a contingent of nuns when they were attacked in present western Kansas by?

418. It was erroneously reported that all were killed in that attack, but all survived except for Sister _____, who reportedly died of what?

419. A cave in Council Grove and a mountain peak near Las Vegas are named for the activities of a religious mystic associated with both. What are the names?

420. The religious mystic whose activities led to those names was?

421. That religious mystic walked the Santa Fe Trail from Council Grove to Las Vegas in 1863, accompanying the wagon train of this Las Vegas merchant?

422. Another important Las Vegas merchant engaged in the Santa Fe trade was?

423. Before Las Vegas, New Mexico, was established as a Santa Fe Trail community in 1835, the first New Mexican town encountered by Trail travelers was?

424. After 1843, however, when it was established, this new settlement replaced Las Vegas as the first New Mexican town encountered by Trail travelers?

425. The first regular mail service over the Santa Fe Trail was begun by the military, from Fort Leavenworth to Santa Fe, in what year?

426. The first contract stagecoach and mail service over the Santa Fe Trail was established in what year?

427. That contract was held by this company?

428. That stage line started from what town?

429. Passenger fare from that point to Santa Fe was how much?

430. What was the baggage allowance per passenger?

431. That first stage company originally had only two stations on the road to Santa Fe, located at?

432. How often did that first stage and mail service depart each end of the Trail?

433. Although the early stage lines were unable to follow schedules closely, the number of days scheduled for the trip from Independence to Santa Fe was?

434. In 1857 how often did stagecoaches depart each end of the Trail?

435. By the 1860s this company was operating stagecoach and mail service on the Trail?

436. That company sent stages from each end of the Trail how often?

437. That company was the first to offer regular stage service over this branch of the Trail?

438. By 1863 the number of days scheduled for the trip from Independence to Santa Fe was?

439. There were old sailors who believed it would be possible to build a sailing wagon to travel the road to Santa Fe, freeing freighters from the need for draft animals. The most famous of these promoters, who actually constructed such a vessel was?

440. What happened to his experimental vessel?

441. This military post in New Mexico, founded in 1851, remained in active service after the Santa Fe Trail was replaced by the railroad?

442. That fort was located near what mountains?

443. Over the years, how many different forts were constructed at that location?

444. The first fort constructed there was built primarily of what materials?

445. The second fort there was an earth embanked forti-

fication known because of its shape as the?

446. Of the last fort constructed there, almost all structures were of adobe; however, which one building contained rooms built of stone?

447. What town on the Santa Fe Trail was located closest to that New Mexico military post?

448. That point was named because it was the junction of these two streams?

449. That name was also appropriate to the Santa Fe Trail for it was the point where?

450. That town began in 1843 on land granted by New Mexican Governor Manuel Armijo to this man and his associates?

451. What is the modern name of that New Mexico town, given the location by railroad surveyors?

452. It was named for this man who settled there in 1849 and operated a store and a ranch?

453. The forerunner of that town was a trading post founded by what two men?

454. That trading post was known as?

455. The trading post was built in what year?

456. The above trading post served as headquarters of a Mr. Kroenig who used what kind of animal to pack merchandise on the Trail?

457. This historic farmstead (now a restored historic site) near Olathe, Kansas, was used as a stagecoach stop on the Trail from 1865-1869 for three different stage lines?

458. The site of this historic community on the Trail in southeastern Colorado was donated to the Pioneer Historical Society of Bent County by Mrs. Alta Page?

459. This historic community contains the homes of these two pioneer settlers?

460. This governor of New Mexico Territory died while traveling east over the Santa Fe Trail?

461. William W. H. Davis, U. S. attorney for New Mexico Territory, traveled by stage over the Santa Fe Trail in 1853 and later (1857) published a book of his experiences, titled?

462. One of the important merchants of the Trail during its final years, this Mexican entrepreneur moved his eastern headquarters seven times as the railroads built westward (from Hays, Kansas, in 1868 to Las Vegas, New Mexico, in 1879)?

463. This man operated a trading ranch near where the Trail crossed Cow Creek in Kansas, at which site his well is still preserved?

464. Because that trader at Cow Creek helped provide buffalo meat for starving families in eastern Kansas during the drought of 1860, he earned the nickname of?

465. Originally called Camp on Pawnee Fork and later known as Camp Alert, the permanent name for the military post was?

466. It was an active post during what years?

467. Fort Lyon, Colorado, was originally named?

468. Fort Lyon was originally located near what trading post?

469. Fort Lyon was an active post during what years?

470. Confederate troops captured Santa Fe during the early years of the Civil War, but they were defeated on the Santa Fe Trail at the Battle of?

471. That battle, because of its significance as the turning point of the war in the region, has been called the?

472. At the time of that battle, Confederate headquarters on the Trail were located at?

473. That ranch was owned by this man from St. Louis, who acquired the ranch in 1858 and sold it in 1869?

474. At the time of that battle, Union headquarters on the Trail were located at?

475. Two days before this major engagement, there had been a small battle between Confederate and Union troops, in which the Confederates were driven from the field. Known by its location, this was the Battle of?

476. During that preliminary battle, the Confederates destroyed what strategic structure, believing they had stopped the Union charge?

477. That belief proved to be untrue because?

478. During the major engagement, located right on the Santa Fe Trail, the Confederates drove the Union forces back, but the Confederates were dealt the critical blow by the destruction of their supply train during the battle by a force led by this major of Colorado Volunteers?

479. The major confrontation between the troops in that battle on the Trail occurred near what ranch?

480. That ranch was the property of this man from St. Louis?

481. What evidence from that famous battle was found near the site of that historic ranch in 1987, 125 years after the battle?

482. In the 1860s Lucien B. Maxwell's home and the headquarters for his ranch, the largest in New Mexico, was located at the site of this New Mexican town through which the Mountain Route of the Trail passed?

483. This famous hotel was built in that New Mexican town during late Trail days and still operates there?

484. This Santa Fe Trail trading firm was opened at that New Mexican town about 1848 and served Trail travelers and regional settlers?

485. This site on the Mountain Branch was once home to Lucien Maxwell and Kit Carson, site of a stage station, site of a military camp in the early 1850s, and is now located on the Philmont Scout Ranch, BSA?

486. This New Mexico creek was the last major stream Trail travelers heading for Santa Fe on the Mountain Branch had to cross before rejoining the Cimarron Cutoff?

487. This Santa Fe Trail landmark and stage station, located west of Council Grove in Kansas, was raided by Missouri bushwhackers in May of 1863?

488. The leader of that raiding party, a follower of William Quantrill, was this former Santa Fe trader?

489. When Joseph Pratt Allyn traveled the Santa Fe Trail in 1863 he reported this about the Arkansas River west of Fort Larned for approximately 100 miles?

490. Two military posts were established on the Santa

Fe Trail during the Civil War to provide protection for the Aubry Route. One of these was _____ on the Arkansas River?

491. The other was _____ south of the Cimarron River?

492. The founder and first commander of that post south of the Cimarron was?

493. This woman, who wrote a splendid book about life on the Trail, spent part of her honeymoon at that military post south of the Cimarron with her soldier husband?

494. The military post founded during the Civil War where the Wet and Dry routes from Pawnee Fork rejoined farther west was?

495. It was an active post during what years?

496. The military post founded during the Civil War near the Walnut Creek crossing of the Trail was?

497. It was an active post during what years?

498. This German woman, bride of an Albuquerque merchant, traveled the Trail to New Mexico in 1863 with ten canaries?

499. In 1867 that woman's mother and brother were killed by Cheyenne Indians while traveling the Trail near this central Kansas landmark?

500. Who was the man who survived an Indian attack near Walnut Creek in Kansas in 1864 and, although he was scalped and left for dead, later earned his living by exhibiting his wound and describing the experience?

501. This attack on an encampment of "peaceful" Cheyenne and Arapaho Indians in Colorado in 1864 was led by the same man who had led the troops that dealt the critical blow to the Confederates in New Mexico in 1862, and it touched off a new wave of Indian hostilities in some areas?

502. Those Indians attacked in 1864 believed they were safe at their encampment, and they were led by this Cheyenne peace chief?

503. In 1867 this general led an expedition against the Indians of the Plains, and visited some of the forts along the Santa Fe Trail. His destruction of a Cheyenne camp on Pawnee Fork probably increased

Indian hostilities that year?

504. This young lieutenant colonel of the newly organized 7th Cavalry led a portion of his regiment on that expedition in 1867?

505. This Kiowa Indian chief led a raid on the horse herd at Fort Dodge in 1867, wearing the uniform of a U. S. major-general which had been presented to him a short time before because of his expressions of peace and friendship?

506. By what was Fort Larned attacked on the evening of August 5, 1868?

507. The only fatality suffered by the garrison during that attack was Corporal Mike McGuillicuddy, 3rd Infantry, who was where when the attack occurred?

508. The Winter Campaign against the southern Plains Indians, 1868-1869, involved forts and troops on the Santa Fe Trail. The Campaign was organized and directed by this military officer?

509. This woman, who traveled the Trail in 1846 while pregnant, was thrown from her carriage at the crossing of Ash Creek, which led to a miscarriage at Bent's Fort a short time later?

510. The physician who accompanied that 1846 caravan and attended her following that accident and through the miscarriage was?

511. A special room at Bent's Fort was built to house what recreational item?

512. William Bent was married to two Cheyenne women, marrying the sister of the first after her death; they were?

513. By these Cheyenne wives William Bent fathered five children; they were?

514. Between 1857 and 1866 this army officer's wife made at least five crossings of the Santa Fe Trail, and her memoirs were published in *I Married a Soldier*?

515. In 1867 this army officer's wife recorded her trip over a portion of the Trail from central Kansas to Fort Union, later published in *An Army Wife on the Frontier*?

516. As railroads built westward from the Missouri River, the eastern end of the Santa Fe Trail moved

westward with the rails; with the completion of the Union Pacific, Eastern Division, to this point north of the old route in 1865, it became the new point of departure for wagon trains?

517. By 1867 that railroad had built to this Kansas town which was the new point of departure for wagon trains?

518. At that time military supplies were shipped by rail to this Kansas fort and forwarded to other forts in the southwest?

519. By 1871 that railroad, known as the Kansas Pacific after 1869, had built to this town in Colorado Territory which was the new point of departure for wagon trains?

520. What railroad built along and replaced the Santa Fe Trail?

521. Which route of the Trail did the railroad follow into New Mexico?

522. The railroad which followed the Santa Fe Trail reached this new town on the Trail in 1872?

523. By 1876 the railroad which followed the Trail reached this town in the new state of Colorado?

524. In 1878 the railroad reached this Colorado town?

525. The railroad began operating over Raton Pass in what year?

526. The town of Santa Fe, Kansas, located near the Santa Fe Trail, was the county seat of this Kansas county from 1887-1920?

527. That county, which contains 27 miles of the Jornada del Muerte of the Cimarron Branch, has the distinction of being the _____ county in Kansas?

528. The town of Santa Fe, Kansas, was abandoned in 1926 because?

529. The town that replaced Santa Fe, Kansas, as the county seat in the county where it was located was?

530. What is located on the former site of Santa Fe, Kansas?

531. Probably the most famous natural landmark along the Santa Fe Trail, located between Walnut Creek and Pawnee Fork, this prominent hill provided a long view of the region and was the site of a popular

campground?

532. West of that famous landmark the Trail divided into two roads which rejoined east of present Dodge City, with one road following closely along the Arkansas River and the other, shorter route following a higher road north of the river. The road along the river was called the?

533. The road away from the river was called the?

534. When the Atchison, Topeka and Santa Fe Railroad was constructed, it followed which of those two routes more closely?

535. One branch of the Oregon Trail followed the Santa Fe Trail until it split off to go north near what present town in Kansas?

536. Excellent remains of Trail ruts may be seen at the "Black Jack" park just east of this Kansas town?

537. "Black Jack" park commemorates a minor incident that happened beside the Santa Fe Trail during the Kansas territorial conflict over slavery, involving this radical antislavery leader?

538. That incident may have been part of the basis for an historically inaccurate movie featuring Ronald Reagan, titled?

539. West of "Black Jack" park there began a narrow divide between waters draining north to the Kansas River and those draining south to the Marias des Cygnes, a ridge known to Trail travelers as?

540. Near the west end of that ridge was this spring, location of the so-called "Wakarusa War" during Kansas territorial days?

541. Located north of present Elkhart, Kansas, this famous spring near the Cimarron River was a campground for Trail travelers?

542. Near that spring is another landmark along the Trail, a prominent projection overlooking the Cimarron valley known as?

543. At the foot of this prominent bluff, John Goose, a soldier during the war with Mexico, was buried after dying from an infection caused by?

544. Another formation along the Trail, with the same name as that in the Cimarron valley, is found in what state?

545. The Cimarron Route of the Trail left the Cimarron River in the present Oklahoma panhandle at an island known as?

546. It was near this point, in October of 1844, that a train belonging to this trader lost over 300 mules to a blizzard and had to remain there until more mules were obtained from Santa Fe?

547. For many years after the loss of those mules at that site, it was reported that passing teamsters did what there?

548. 1844 must have been a bad year for that trader because, after securing more mules from New Mexico he found no market for his goods there and headed on to Chihuahua, only to lose most of his mules again.   This time he lost them to?

549. Unlike Lower and Middle Cimarron Springs, Upper Cimarron Spring is?

550. West of Upper Cimarron Spring was this spring, considered to have the best water since leaving the Arkansas River and beside which is located a register cliff containing names of some of the Trail travelers?

551. This famous Trail landmark, a peak located near present Clayton, New Mexico, was named for a Cheyenne Indian chief who was reportedly buried there?

552. Another Trail landmark, located near present Clayton and west of Mt. Dora and sometimes called Mt. Clayton, is this formation included in a well-known sketch in Josiah Gregg's *Commerce of the Prairies*?

553. What five landmarks along the Santa Fe Trail are recognized on the National Register of Historic Places in the Clayton Complex?

554. This famous Trail landmark, located south of present Springer, New Mexico, received its name because it appeared to be what it is called when viewed from a distance?

555. This famous spring, located near that landmark, was an important campsite on the Trail?

556. An attack on the east-bound stagecoach occurred at this spring in 1850, in which all ten members

of the party were killed. The attackers were?

557. The attack is known as the?

558. Much of what was the Cimarron Route, particularly the western end of it, was probably well-known and used as a route of travel prior to the opening of the Santa Fe Trail by Indians and Mexican *Ciboleros* or?

559. El Vado de las Piedras refers to the stone crossing of this New Mexico river?

560. Post Office Oak, where Santa Fe Trail travelers left letters to be picked up and delivered by other travelers, was located where?

561. When the Santa Fe Trail was opened it passed through a region which later was contained within five states; what were those states and in what years were they admitted to the Union?

562. This military post was established in Santa Fe soon after the U. S. occupation of the western terminus of the Trail in 1846?

563. For what is Sgt. Frank Gibson, Co. D, 19th Infantry, especially remembered at Fort Larned?

564. What former military post on the Santa Fe Trail is now used as a state soldiers' home?

565. This famous adobe trading fort on the Mountain Branch of the Trail has been reconstructed by the National Park Service?

566. This New Mexican state senator served as president of the Highway 56 Santa Fe Trail Association and promoted preservation and recognition of Trail sites, including those around his hometown of Clayton (Clayton Complex)?

567. What two women erected special markers along the Santa Fe Trail in Douglas County, Kansas?

568. Who is the author of *Following the Santa Fe Trail: A guide for Modern Travelers*?

569. This fine museum and research center is devoted to understanding the entire Santa Fe Trail and its history, the only such institution that exists today?

570. What organization was founded at Trinidad, Colorado, in 1986, to help preserve, protect, and promote the Santa Fe Trail and its history?

571. Who was the first president of that organization?

572. What is the official publication of that organization called?

573. At this Missouri State Historic Site, early history of the Santa Fe Trail is commemorated along with several historic buildings, including the George Caleb Bingham home and the Huston Tavern?

574. This historic site in Missouri has been partiallly reconstructed as it was when wagon trains organized there and the survey of the Trail began there?

575. During the late 1850s William Allison operated a trading ranch near where the Trail crossed this Kansas stream?

576. It was at that trading ranch in 1859 that this Kiowa sub-chief became intoxicated, tried to murder the rancher, was captured by cavalry troops sent to protect the ranch, and was shot to death while trying to escape?

577. A few days later, probably in retaliation for the death of their sub-chief, a party of Kiowas attacked the mail coach near Pawnee Fork and killed two of the three-man crew. William Cole survived the attack, but these two brothers were killed?

578. On January 2, 1861, a detachment of troops sent out from Fort Union, New Mexico, to find and punish Kiowas and Comanches who were raiding along the Trail, suprised a large encampment of those Indians a few miles north of this Trail site and killed several of the Indians, destroyed the captured encampment, and captured about 40 horses?

579. During the early 1860s W. D. Wheeler maintained a trading ranch and toll bridge where the Trail crossed this Kansas stream?

580. In 1867 a military encampment was established at that crossing and named?

581. That encampment was garrisoned by a company of the 10th Cavalry, members of which were called "Buffalo Soldiers" because?

582. What National Historic Site is located on the old Trail in Colorado?

583. What two historic National Monuments are located on the old Trail in New Mexico?

584. What National Historic Site is located on the old Trail in Kansas?

585. What noted student of western trails prepared new maps of the Santa Fe National Historic Trail and wrote several books about the route?

586. Because of their work in promoting the Santa Fe Trail, two people were awarded the title of Santa Fe Trail Ambassador by the Santa Fe Trail Association in 1987. Who were they?

587. Of those two, which one has walked the route to Santa Fe and driven a small wagon over the Trail?

588. What was the first regional chapter organized and affiliated with the Santa Fe Trail Association?

589. Where was this chapter located?

590. The historic Baca House in Trinidad, Colorado, was originally built by this Santa Fe trader?

591. That house in Trinidad was so admired by this Trail figure that he had one just like built at his ranch at Raton Pass?

592. A stagecoach that was used on the Santa Fe Trail is on display at the Palace of the Governors Museum in Santa Fe. This coach was used by what stage company?

593. This particular coach was involved in a famous holdup on Raton Pass in 1867 by this gang?

594. How much loot was reportedly taken in that holdup?

595. What happened to the leader of the gang that held up the stage?

596. A few miles west of the Cottonwood Crossing was a place known as Cottonwood Hole, where in the 1860s a trading post was established and known as?

597. The first trading post on the Santa Fe Trail in Kansas to be established west of Council Grove was located near the Turkey Creek Crossing in 1855 by?

598. Frank and William Hartwell operated a stage station near the Trail crossing of this creek for a short time in the 1860s?

599. The Hartwell brothers moved farther west after a change in the stage operations bypassed their old station, and they established another station west

of Fort Dodge at the?

600. The bullwhackers whips, by which they they
      encouraged the oxen pulling wagons on the Trail
      with the loud cracks of the rawhide or buckskin
      thong at the end, were commonly known by this
      name?

601. In what year did a trade caravan first use oxen
      for the trip from Missouri to Santa Fe?

602. Originally known as Lookout Hill, what is the later
      and common name of the hill that overlooks the "Dry
      Route" crossing of Pawnee Fork west of present
      Larned, Kansas?

603. Who operated a trading ranch and saloon at the "Dry
      Route" crossing of Pawnee Fork in the 1860s?

604. By what euphemism was the saloon at the "Dry
      Route" crossing of Pawnee Fork, where gambling
      and prostitutes were available, known to the sol-
      diers stationed at Fort Larned?

605. In what year did Josiah Gregg make his first trip
      over the Santa Fe Trail?

606. In 1838 a group of investors, including several men
      engaged in the Santa Fe trade, purchased the site
      of Westport Landing on the Missouri River to estab-
      lish what town?

607. Upper Cimarron Spring in present Oklahoma was
      also known by this name?

608. A group of Chihuahua merchants traveled across
      Texas in 1839 on their way east to purchase trade
      items. When they returned via the same route the
      following year, with what did they return in addition
      to the usual trade items?

609. What newspaper in Franklin, Missouri, carried
      accounts of the opening of the road to Santa Fe in
      the early 1820s?

610. Who was the member of the 1825 Santa Fe Trail
      survey crew who was the father of the man later
      known as the greatest freighter on the Trail?

611. Although 1831 is noted in Trail history as the year
      in which famed mountain man Jedidiah Smith was
      killed by Indians on the Santa Fe Trail, this young
      man of the same expedition was killed by Indians
      near Pawnee Fork a few days before Smith died?

612. The grave of Henry Lorenzen, 1837-1879, is located just west of where the Cimarron Cutoff Route crossed this New Mexico stream at the famous "Rock Crossing"?

613. Known as Wah-to-Yah and the Breasts of the Earth, these famous peaks were visible to Trail travelers on the Mountain Branch for great distances?

614. Richens Lacy ("Uncle Dick") Wootton later claimed that, on his first trip on the Santa Fe Trail in 1836 while standing night guard, he mistook what for an Indian and shot it?

615. On what stream in present Rice County, Kansas, was Wootton camped when he fired at what he thought was an Indian?

616. In 1853 an army officer and his family brought this musical instrument over the Santa Fe Trail to Fort Union, New Mexico?

617. Who was the army officer who served as military storekeeper in charge of the arsenal at Fort Union, New Mexico, and remained at the site near the Trail after the arsenal was closed and he had retired?

618. In the 1870s the Sisters of Loretto built what famous chapel in Santa Fe, facing the old Santa Fe Trail?

619. For what "miraculous" structure is that famous chapel of the Sisters of Loretto in Santa Fe known?

620. In old Westport, present Kansas City, Missouri, in Pioneer Park where a large terrazzo map showing the trails going west is located, a recent larger-than-life statue by Tom Beard features these three pioneers?

621. What museum in Lyons, Kansas, contains exhibits on the Santa Fe Trail and Coronado's visit to Quivira?

622. What stone building was reconstructed at Fort Larned National Historic Site in 1988?

623. What modern U.S. highway follows a considerable portion of the old Santa Fe Trail (Cimarron Cutoff)?

SUGGESTED READINGS

Barry, Louise, comp. *The Beginning of the West: Annals of the Kansas Gateway to the American West, 1540-1854.* Topeka: Kansas State Historical Society, 1972.

Beachum, Larry M. *William Becknell, Father of the Santa Fe Trade.* El Paso: Texas Western Press, 1982.

Brown, William E. *The Santa Fe Trail.* Reprint, St. Louis: Patrice Press, 1988.

Chaput, Donald. *Francois X. Aubry; Trader, Trailmaker and Voyageur in the Southwest, 1846-1854.* Glendale: Arthur H. Clark Co., 1975.

Connor, Seymour V. and Jimmy M. Skaggs. *Broadcloth and Britches: The Santa Fe Trade.* College Station: Texas A & M University Press, 1977.

DeVoto, Bernard. *The Year of Decision: 1846.* Boston: Little, Brown and Co., 1943.

Drumm, Stella M., ed. *Down the Santa Fe Trail and into Mexico: The Diary of Susan Shelby Magoffin, 1846-1847.* New Haven: Yale University Press, 1926; Lincoln: University of Nebraska Press, 1982 (paper edition).

Duffus, R. L. *The Santa Fe Trail.* New York: Longmans, Green & Co., 1931; Albuquerque: University of New Mexico Press, 1972 (paper edition).

Emmett, Chris. *Fort Union and the Winning of the Southwest.* Norman: University of Oklahoma Press, 1965.

Franzwa, Gregory M. *Images of the Santa Fe Trail.* St. Louis: Patrice Press, 1988.

Franzwa, Gregory M. *Impressions of the Santa Fe Trail.* St. Louis: Patrice Press, 1988.

Garrard, Lewis H. *Wah-to-Yah and the Taos Trail.* Reprint, Norman: University of Oklahoma Press, 1955.

Gregg, Josiah. *Commerce of the Prairies.* Ed. by Max L. Moorhead. Norman: University of Oklahoma Press, 1954. An abridged paper edition, ed. by Milo M. Quaife, is available from Lincoln: University of Nebraska Press, 1967.

Gregg, Kate L., ed. *The Road to Santa Fe.* Albuquerque: University of New Mexico Press, 1952.

Hulbert, Archer B., ed. *Southwest on the Turquoise Trail: The First Diaries on the Road to Santa Fe.* Denver: Denver Public Library, 1933.

Lavender, David. *Bent's Fort.* New York: Doubleday & Co., 1954.

Martin, Gene and Mary Martin. *Trail Dust: A Quick Picture History of the Santa Fe Trail.* Boulder: Johnson Publishing Company, 1972.

Moorhead, Max L. *New Mexico's Royal Road: Trade and Travel on the Chihuahua Trail.* Norman: University of Oklahoma Press, 1958.

Oliva, Leo E., ed. *Adventure on the Santa Fe Trail.* Topeka: Kansas State Historical Society, 1988.

Oliva, Leo E. *Fort Larned on the Santa Fe Trail.* Topeka: Kansas State Historical Society, 1982.

Oliva, Leo E. *Soldiers on the Santa Fe Trail.* Norman: University of Oklahoma Press, 1967.

Rittenhouse, Jack D. *Trail of Commerce and Conquest: A Brief History of the Road to Santa Fe.* Reprint, Woodston: Santa Fe Trail Association, 1987.

Russell, Marian Sloan. *Land of Enchantment: Memoirs of Marian Russell Along the Santa Fe Trail.* Reprint, Albuquerque: University of New Mexico Press, 1981.

Simmons, Marc. *Following the Santa Fe Trail: A Guide for Modern Travelers.* New rev. ed., Santa Fe: Ancient City Press, 1986.

Simmons, Marc. *Murder on the Santa Fe Trail: An International Incident, 1843.* El Paso: Texas Western Press, 1987.

Simmons, Marc, ed. *On the Santa Fe Trail.* Lawrence: University Press of Kansas, 1986.

Stocking, Hobart E. *The Road to Santa Fe.* New York: Hastings House, 1971.

Strate, David K., ed. *West by Southwest: Letters of Joseph Pratt Allyn, a Traveller Along the Santa Fe Trail, 1863.* Dodge City: Kansas Heritage Center, 1984.

Sunder, John E. *Matt Field on the Santa Fe Trail.* Norman: Univeristy of Oklahoma Press, 1960.

Taylor, Morris F. *First Mail West: Stagecoach Lines on the Santa Fe Trail.* Albuquerque: University of New Mexico Press, 1971.

Utley, Robert M. *Fort Union National Monument, New Mexico.* Washington: National Park Service, 1962.

Walker, Henry P. *The Wagonmasters: High Plains Freighting from the Earliest Days of the Santa Fe Trail to 1880.* Norman: University of Oklahoma Press, 1966.

Wetzel, David N., ed. *The Santa Fe Trail: New Perspectives.* Denver: Colorado Historical Society, 1987.

SANTA FE TRAIL ANSWERS

1. May 8, 1987
2. *Commerce of the Prairies*
3. Josiah Gregg
4. 1821
5. Mexico achieved independence from Spain and Missouri became a state
6. James Monroe
7. William Becknell
8. Ezekiel Williams
9. Governor Facundo Melgares
10. Fur trapper
11. Competition in the trade with Santa Fe had reduced the potential for profits
12. Commerce
13. The route of conquest of territory from Mexico (including New Mexico, Arizona, and California)
14. Emigration to the Southwest
15. Stephen Watts Kearny
16. 1880
17. Rutherford B. Hayes
18. Daughters of the American Revolution (DAR)
19. Fanny Geiger Thompson
20. Burlingame, Kansas
21. 175
22. Kansas
23. 100
24. Mary B. and Leo E. Gamble
25. The DAR marker at Cañoncito
26. Schools
27. American Pioneer Trails Association

28. 1948
29. Irvin Shope
30. Coronado
31. Quivira
32. Little Arkansas River
33. Quivirans
34. Juan de Padilla
35. Council Grove, Herington, and Lyons, Kansas
36. Juan de Oñate
37. 1821
38. Franklin
39. Boon's Lick Road
40. 1816
41. 1819
42. *Independence*
43. 900
44. 1829
45. New Franklin
46. Boonville
47. Cooper's Fort
48. Arrow Rock
49. Osage Trace
50. Missionary Road
51. Lexington
52. John, James, and Robert Aull
53. Richmond, Liberty, and Independence
54. Chihuahua City
55. Keelboats
56. Dr. John Sappington
57. George Caleb Bingham
58. Meredith Miles Marmaduke
59. 1825
60. Fort Osage
61. 1808
62. William Clark

63. Government Factory (trading post)
64. George C. Sibley
65. Military post
66. George C. Sibley
67. Joseph C. Brown
68. William Becknell
69. They were filed away in Washington and not used until later by historians of the Trail
70. Kate L. Gregg
71. *The Road to Santa Fe*
72. Blue Mills Landing
73. Wayne City Landing
74. Independence, Missouri
75. Jackson County
76. Robert Weston
77. Oregon and California
78. Westport, Missouri
79. New Santa Fe
80. William Ray
81. Cave Spring
82. Red Bridge Crossing
83. Minor Park
84. Fort Leavenworth
85. Grinter Ferry, operated by Moses Grinter
86. Neff Tavern, operated by Isaac Neff and family
87. Lone Elm
88. Fort Osage
89. Oak Creek
90. Fry McGee
91. Burlingame
92. John Switzler; Switzler Creek
93. I. B. Titus
94. Dragoon Creek
95. Soldier Creek
96. Council Grove

97. Dry Turkey Creek
98. Seth Hays
99. Ralph Hathaway
100. Plum Buttes
101. Arkansas River
102. Cimarron River
103. Bent's Fort
104. Mulberry Creek
105. Cimarron and Ingalls, Kansas
106. Chouteau's Island
107. Indian Mound
108. La Jornada del Muerte (The Journey of Death)
109. 1834
110. Plaza
111. Rock Corral
112. Paul and Pierre Mallet
113. Pierre Satren, Louis Febre, and Joseph Riballo
114. Felipe de Sandoval
115. Fort Cavagnial
116. Pedro Vial
117. Josef Villanueva and Vincente Espinosa
118. Baptiste Lalande and Jeannot Metoyer
119. Zebulon M. Pike
120. General James Wilkinson
121. Facundo Melgares
122. John Hamilton Robinson
123. Jacques Clamorgan
124. Robert McKnight, James Baird, Benjamin Shreve, and Michael McDonough
125. David Meriwether
126. Pawnee Indians
127. Territorial Governor of New Mexico, with his office in the Palace of the Governors
128. The ceiling of the cell where he had been imprisoned in 1820 collapsed
129. John R. Peyton

130. Charles Lucas
131. Annette Jimenez
132. St. Louis
133. 1609 or 1610
134. La Villa Real de Santa Fe
135. Royal City of Holy Faith
136. Rio Santa Fe
137. Palace of the Governors
138. Santa Fe Plaza
139. San Miguel
140. Adobe bricks
141. Pecos Pueblo
142. Kiva
143. 1680
144. Popé
145. General Diego de Vargas
146. Greer Garson Fogelson
147. John McKnight and Thomas James
148. 1822
149. Fort Osage
150. William Becknell
151. $700
152. Conestoga
153. Osnaburg
154. Murphy Wagon
155. 5,000 pounds
156. Light Blue
157. Red
158. Pine tar and tallow
159. Leaders
160. Wheelers
161. Swing teams
162. Haw!
163. Gee!
164. Whoa!

165. Hugh Glenn and Jacob Fowler
166. A grizzly bear
167. The Caches
168. Blood and/or liquid in the stomach of a buffalo they killed
169. Chihuahua
170. Augustus Storrs
171. M. M. Marmaduke
172. Walnut Creek
173. San Miguel
174. Santa Fe Trail
175. Pecos River
176. 25%
177. $500 to $950
178. Pack more commodities per wagon, use a larger wagon, or consolidate wagon loads a short distance from the point where customs were collected
179. 1824
180. Missionary Ridge
181. Captain
182. Mora River
183. Water, grass, and wood
184. Kansa, Osage, Sioux, Cheyenne, Crow, Otoe, Missouri, Pawnee, and Omaha
185. Chouteau's Island
186. Taos
187. Andrew Broadus
188. Richard Gentry
189. Josefa Jarmillo
190. Taos
191. Charles Bent
192. One dollar
193. Diamond Spring
194. Frèmont Spring
195. Jack Costello
196. Little Arkansas River

197. Major Alphonso Wetmore
198. Shot his own mule through the head
199. Cloth, metal tools, notions, jewelry, religious objects, guns and ammunition, and wagons
200. Hudson Bay blanket
201. Gold and silver specie, silver bullion, gold dust, mules, donkeys, furs, buffalo robes, and wool
202. Felt hat
203. $8 to $10 per hundred pounds
204. 1834
205. Father José Antonio Martinez
206. *El Crepúsculo de la Libertad* (*The Dawn of Liberty*)
207. James L. Collins
208. *Gazette*
209. 1869
210. 1856
211. Horses, mules, and oxen
212. Oxen
213. Horses
214. "Catch Up! Catch Up!"
215. "Stretch Out! Stretch Out!"
216. $25 per month and board
217. Flour, salt pork, coffee, and fresh meat killed along the way
218. Flies and mosquitoes
219. Two or four columns
220. 15 miles
221. McNees (first name unknown, after whom McNees Crossing was named) and Daniel Munroe
222. Louise Creek
223. Corrumpa Creek
224. John Means
225. Bvt. Maj. Bennet Riley
226. Oxen
227. Bullwhackers

228. Charles (captain) and William Bent
229. Samuel C. Lamme
230. Col. José Antonio Viscarra
231. Richard Gentry
232. Jedediah Smith
233. Lower Cimarron Spring
234. Middle Crossing and Upper Crossing
235. Independence Day, July 4, 1831
236. Mounted Rangers
237. Capt. William N. Wickliffe
238. U. S. Dragoons
239. Capt. Clifton Wharton
240. Col. Henry Dodge
241. Samuel Hunt
242. Edward Miller
243. Matthew "Matt" C. Field
244. Frederick A. Wislizenus
245. Cottonwood River
246. Colonel Edwin V. Sumner
247. Dr. Michael Steck
248. Aubry Route
249. Using their own blankets to cover the mules during the storm
250. *Lebanon*
251. Manuel Armijo
252. 1841
253. General Hugh McLeod
254. George W. Kendall
255. *Uncle Tom's Cabin*
256. Governor Manuel Armijo
257. Antonio José Chávez
258. John McDaniel
259. Philip St. George Cooke
260. Black Pool
261. Ford or Dodge City

262. Jacob Snively
263. Charles A. Warfield
264. Philip St. George Cooke
265. 1844
266. Fort Leavenworth
267. Stephen Watts Kearny
268. 2,000 miles
269. 99 days
270. None
271. Tariffs
272. 1845
273. Lts. James W. Abert and William G. Peck
274. Thomas Fitzpatrick
275. John C. Frèmont
276. Christopher "Kit" Carson
277. Trinchera Pass
278. Two Buttes Fork
279. 1851
280. Lieutenant John Pope
281. Holly, Colorado
282. Granada, Colorado
283. Canadian River
284. 1846
285. Civil War, 1861–1865
286. Kiowas and Comanches
287. Fort Lyon, Colorado
288. Richens Lacy Wootton
289. "Uncle Dick" Wootton
290. 1865 is the generally accepted date, although some references to it being there earlier have been found
291. $1.50
292. Indians
293. Purgatoire River; also called Purgatory and Pick-etwire River
294. Hole in the Rock

295. A dam constructed by the railroad filled with silt and covered the site
296. Hole in the Prairie
297. Trinidad, Colorado
298. Fisher's Peak (originally Raton Peak)
299. Cruz Torres
300. Raton, New Mexico
301. Willow Springs
302. Clifton House
303. General James H. Carleton
304. General Samuel R. Curtis
305. Forts Aubry, Dodge, Larned, Lyon, Union, and Zarah
306. Camp Nichols
307. Dr. Eugene Leitensdorfer
308. Soledad Abreu
309. 1846
310. The Land of Enchantment
311. Francis X. Aubry
312. 5 days and 22 hours
313. El Camino Real, New Mexico's Royal Road, or the Chihuahua Trail
314. 1824
315. Manuel S. Escudero
316. Manuel Alvarez
317. New York City
318. Philadelphia, Pennsylvania
319. Peter Harmony, Nephews and Company
320. Ojo de Gallinas and Rio Gallinas
321. Las Vegas, New Mexico
322. 1835
323. Sangre de Cristo
324. Blood of Christ
325. Glorieta Pass
326. Francis Parkman
327. Mexico

328. James K. Polk
329. William L. Marcy
330. The Army of the West
331. Colonel Alexander W. Doniphan
332. Richmond
333. Mountain Route
334. Bent's Old Fort
335. Lt. William H. Emory
336. August 18, 1846
337. Governor Manuel Armijo
338. Dona Gertrudes Barcelo
339. *La Tules*
340. Treaty of Guadalupe Hidalgo
341. $5,000,000
342. Seligman Brothers (Sigmund and Bernard)
343. Ten million dollars
344. Historical Society of New Mexico
345. 1859
346. $10,000,000
347. $40,000,000
348. Scurvy
349. Vitamin C
350. Chili peppers
351. Mexico
352. James Browne
353. $11.75 per hundred pounds
354. James Browne and William H. Russell
355. Joseph Clymer and David Waldo
356. Alexander Majors
357. Russell, Majors and Waddell
358. Lexington, Missouri
359. A cannon ball fired during the Civil War is lodged in one of the columns
360. One dollar per day plus board
361. Mary Watt Dodson Donoho, wife of William Donoho

362. 1833
363. Mary A. Donoho
364. Operate a hotel on the plaza
365. Harriet Donoho (born in 1835) and James B. Donoho (born in 1837)
366. 1837
367. Mrs. Rachael Plummer, Mrs. John Horn, and a Mrs. Harris
368. Susan Shelby Magoffin
369. Isaac Shelby
370. Marian Sloan Russell
371. New Mexico Art Museum
372. Maid Marian
373. Fort Union
374. Tecolote
375. Trinidad, Colorado
376. Lexington, Missouri; Council Grove, Kansas; and Lamar, Colorado
377. Albuquerque, New Mexico
378. Julia Archibald Holmes
379. Secretary of New Mexico Territory
380. James Holmes
381. John Mix Stanley
382. Major Thomas Swords
383. James Wiley Magoffin
384. Maria Gertrudis Valdes de Beremende
385. Captain Philip St. George Cooke
386. Diego Archuleta
387. Taos Revolt or Taos Uprising, 1847
388. Dr. Henry Connelly
389. Territorial Governor
390. Mariano José Chávez
391. Dolores Perea
392. Samuel Owens (in battle) and James Aull (assassinated by thieves)
393. Albert Speyer and James J. Webb

394. Council Grove
395. Sterling Price
396. Mormon Battalion
397. Cimarron Route
398. Captain Philip St. George Cooke
399. Charles Bent
400. Thomas Fitzpatrick
401. Fort Mann
402. Seth Hays
403. Malcolm Conn
404. Last Chance Store
405. William Gilpin
406. Fort Mann
407. Gold
408. Caroline Newcome (enlisted as Bill Newcome)
409. $16
410. Ceran St. Vrain
411. James P. Beckwourth
412. Asiatic Cholera
413. Bent's Old Fort
414. James White
415. Fort Atkinson
416. Rev. Jean B. Lamy
417. Comanche Indians
418. Sister Alphonsa Thompson died of fright
419. Hermit's Cave in Council Grove and Hermit's Peak near Las Vegas
420. Giovanni Maria Augustini
421. Eugenio Romero
422. José Albino Baca
423. San Miguel
424. La Junta
425. 1849
426. 1850
427. Waldo, Hall and Company

428. Independence, Missouri
429. $125 during the summer season and $150 during the winter months
430. 40 pounds
431. New Santa Fe and Council Grove
432. Monthly
433. 25 days
434. Semi-monthly
435. Barlow-Sanderson Overland Mail and Express Company
436. Weekly
437. Mountain Route
438. 14 days
439. "Windwagon" Thomas
440. It crashed during its maiden voyage
441. Fort Union
442. Turkey Mountains
443. Three
444. Logs
445. Star Fort
446. Guardhouse or jail
447. La Junta (The Junction)
448. Mora River and Sapello Creek
449. The Cimarron and Mountain routes rejoined
450. John Scolly
451. Watrous
452. Samuel B. Watrous
453. Alexander Barclay and Joseph Doyle
454. Barclay's Fort
455. 1849
456. Camel
457. Mahaffie Farmstead and Stagecoach Stop
458. Boggsville, Colorado
459. Thomas O. Boggs and John W. Prowers
460. James S. Calhoun

461. *El Gringo*
462. Miguel Antonio Otero
463. William Mathewson
464. "Buffalo Bill" (a name later applied to William F. Cody, too)
465. Fort Larned
466. 1859-1878
467. Fort Wise
468. Bent's New Fort
469. 1860-1889
470. Battle of Glorieta Pass
471. Gettysburg of the West
472. Johnson's Ranch
473. Anthony P. Johnson
474. Kozlowski's Ranch
475. Apache Canyon
476. Bridge
477. Union troops jumped their horses across the open chasm and captured a large number of Confederates
478. Major John M. Chivington
479. Pigeon's Ranch
480. Alexander Valle
481. The remains of more than 30 Confederates killed during the battle and buried on the site
482. Cimarron, New Mexico
483. St. James Hotel
484. Dahl Brothers Trading Post
485. Rayado, New Mexico
486. Ocate Creek
487. Diamond Springs
488. Dick Yeager
489. The river was dry throughout that distance
490. Fort Aubry
491. Camp Nichols
492. Christopher "Kit" Carson

493. Marian Sloan Russell
494. Fort Dodge
495. 1864-1882
496. Fort Zarah
497. 1864-1869
498. Ernestine Huning
499. Plum Buttes
500. Robert McGee
501. Sand Creek (Sand Creek Massacre)
502. Black Kettle
503. Major General Winfield S. Hancock
504. Lt. Col. George A. Custer
505. Satanta
506. A rabid wolf
507. Corporal McGuillicuddy was a patient in the Fort Larned Hospital when he was bitten by the rabid wolf
508. Major General Philip H. Sheridan
509. Susan Shelby Magoffin
510. Dr. Phillipe Auguste Masure
511. Billiard table
512. Owl Woman and Yellow Woman
513. Robert, George, Julia, Charles, and Mary
514. Lydia Spencer Lane
515. Alice Blackwood Baldwin
516. Junction City, Kansas
517. Hays, Kansas
518. Fort Hays
519. Kit Carson, Colorado Territory
520. Atchison, Topeka and Santa Fe Railroad
521. Mountain Branch
522. Dodge City, Kansas
523. La Junta, Colorado
524. Trinidad, Colorado
525. 1879

526. Haskell County
527. Flattest or most level county in Kansas
528. The railroad never built to it
529. Sublette, Kansas
530. Old Santa Fe Feedyards
531. Pawnee Rock
532. Wet Route
533. Dry Route
534. Wet Route
535. Gardner, Kansas
536. Baldwin City, Kansas
537. John Brown
538. *The Santa Fe Trail*
539. The Narrows
540. Hickory Spring
541. Middle Spring
542. Point of Rocks
543. A Tarantula bite
544. New Mexico (Point of Rocks located west of Clayton or east of Springer)
545. Willow Bar
546. Albert Speyer
547. Arranged the bones in different patterns on the ground
548. Navajos
549. Not located on the Cimarron River but is six miles south of it
550. Cold Spring
551. Rabbit Ears
552. Round Mound
553. McNees Crossing, Rabbit Ears, Mt. Dora, Round Mound, and Turkey Creek Crossing
554. Wagon Mound
555. Santa Clara Spring
556. Jicarilla Apache and Ute Indians
557. Wagon Mound Massacre

558. Mexican buffalo hunters
559. Canadian River
560. Council Grove, Kansas
561. Missouri (1821), Kansas (1861), Colorado (1876), Oklahoma (1907), and New Mexico (1912)
562. Fort Marcy
563. His name is carved into every remaining original stone building at Fort Larned
564. Fort Dodge, Kansas
565. Bent's Old Fort
566. William Wheatley
567. Katharine B. Kelley and Amelia J. Betts
568. Marc Simmons
569. Santa Fe Trail Center, Larned, Kansas
570. Santa Fe Trail Association
571. Marc Simmons
572. *Wagon Tracks*
573. Arrow Rock State Historic Site
574. Fort Osage, Missouri
575. Walnut Creek
576. Pawnee
577. Lawrence and Michael Smith
578. Cold Spring (in present Oklahoma panhandle)
579. Little Arkansas River
580. Camp Grierson
581. The 10th Cavalry regiment was comprised of Black soldiers as was the 9th Cavalry, and both regiments were called "Buffalo Soldiers" by the Indians and adopted that nickname
582. Bent's Old Fort National Historic Site
583. Fort Union National Monument and Pecos Pueblo National Monument
584. Fort Larned National Historic Site
585. Gregory M. Franzwa
586. Paul Bentrup and Les Vilda
587. Les Vilda

588. Cimarron Cutoff Chapter
589. The Cimarron Cutoff Chapter included four counties in four states: Baca County, Colorado; Morton County, Kansas; Union County, New Mexico; and Cimarron County, Oklahoma
590. John Simpson Hough
591. Richins Lacy (Uncle Dick) Wootton
592. Barlow and Sanderson
593. Kid Barton Gang
594. $60,000
595. Kid Barton was captured and hanged from a railroad bridge near Tucumcari, New Mexico
596. "French Frank's" (after owner Frank Laloge)
597. Charles O. Fuller
598. Six Mile Creek
599. Cimarron Crossing
600. "Missouri Pistols"
601. 1830
602. Jenkin's Hill
603. A. H. Boyd
604. Hog Ranch
605. 1831
606. Kansas, which later became Kansas City, Missouri
607. Flag Spring
608. A Circus
609. *Missouri Intelligencer*
610. Benjamin Majors (father of Alexander Majors)
611. E. S. Minter
612. Canadian River
613. Spanish Peaks
614. A mule named "Old Jack"
615. Little Cow Creek
616. Piano
617. Captain William R. Shoemaker
618. Chapel of Our Lady of Light (or Loretto Chapel)
619. Spiral staircase to the choir loft

620. Alexander Majors, Jim Bridger, and John Calvin McCoy
621. Coronado-Quivira Museum
622. Blockhouse
623. U.S. Highway 56

An invitation to join the

SANTA FE TRAIL ASSOCIATION

■Everyone interested in the history and preservation of the Santa Fe Trail is cordially invited to join the Santa Fe Trail Association. This organization was formally established during the first Trail Symposium held in Trinidad, Colorado, at the foot of Raton Pass during September 1986.

■Its purpose is to promote public awareness of and appreciation for this historic pioneer route by developing a variety of commemorative and educational activities.

■Your membership helps provide the support needed to carry out the Association's programs.

■Each member receives a membership card, an annual roster of all members, and the quarterly newsletter, *Wagon Tracks*.

■A main feature of Association activity is the biennial Symposium, in odd-numbered years, at which dedicated Trail enthusiasts gather to exchange views and make new friendships during lectures, panels, field trips, and social gatherings.

■Won't you join us by making a copy of the form on the back of this page, completing it, and returning it to the Association?

"The Santa Fe Trail lives on!"
Marc Simmons
Keynote Address, 1986 Symposium

To join the Association, please copy the form below and send it with your dues. Thank you.

Membership Application

SANTA FE TRAIL ASSOCIATION

Ruth Olson, Sec.-Treas.
Santa Fe Trail Center
RR 3, Larned, KS 67550

☐ Enroll me as a member for the year _____

Name(s) _____

Address _____

City, State, Zip _____

Telephone (____) _____

All memberships expire on December 31.
Please make checks to Santa Fe Trail Association.

☐ New Member   ☐ Renewal

Membership Categories
(check one)

☐ **Benefactor**   **$1,000**
☐ **Patron**   **$100/year**
☐ **Institutional**   **$25/year**
☐ **Family**   **$15/year**
☐ **Individual**   **$10/year**

☐ Check here if you are willing to serve on a committee.

Special Interests: _____